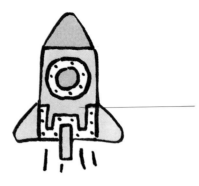

Also by Maureen Roffey

What's the Time?
What's the Weather?
How Many?
Home Sweet Home
Look, There's My Hat!

Copyright © 1995 by Maureen Roffey
All rights reserved.
The right of Maureen Roffey to be identified as
the author of this work has been asserted
by her in accordance with the Copyright,
Designs and Patents Act 1988.
This edition first published in Great Britain in 1995
by Macmillan Children's Books, a division of
Macmillan Publishers Limited, Cavaye Place,
London SW10 and Basingstoke and
associated companies worldwide.

ISBN 0 333 58344 2 (hb)

ISBN 0 333 59233 6 (pb)

A CIP catalogue record for this book is
available from the British Library.
Printed in Singapore.

How Do We Get There?

Maureen Roffey

MACMILLAN CHILDREN'S BOOKS

We are going shopping.

How do we get there?

We get there by car.

We are going to school.

there?

We get t

We are going to visit granny.

How do we get there?

We get there by train.

We are going on holiday.

DEPARTURES

How do we get there?

We get there by
aeroplane.

We are going across the sea.

How do we get there?

We get there by boat.

We are going to the moon.

How do we get there?

We get there by rocket, of course!